KT-491-559

...me!

Contains
SERIOUSLY SCIENCEY
experiments

WARNING: Some MESSY
stuff inside. Ask a grown-up
before you start!

BY **JANE CLARKE** ILLUSTRATED BY **JAMES BROWN**

AL'S AWESOME SCIENCE

Egg-speriments!

FIVE QUILLS

Mrs Good

Mr Good

Precious

Also starring these guys!

For my scientific son, Andrew – J.C.

For Pam and John (who love dogs) xxx – J.B.

AL'S AWESOME SCIENCE: EGG-SPERIMENTS!

First published in Great Britain in 2017 by Five Quills
93 Oakwood Court, London W14 8JZ

www.fivequills.co.uk

Five Quills is a trademark of Five Quills

Edited by Natascha Biebow at Blue Elephant Storyshaping
Designed by Becky Chilcott

A CIP record for this title is available from the British Library

ISBN 978 0 9935537 3 8

1 3 5 7 9 10 8 6 4 2

Printed and bound in Great Britain by Clays Ltd, St Ives plc

CONTENTS

Hatching a Plan

THWACK! Al's experiment had begun!

Mushy green bits splattered down from the storeroom ceiling.

"Mangled molecules!" Al muttered.

He hadn't realised there were any lettuces left in that box. He tightened his grip on Great Grandpa Boffin's walking stick.

THWACK!

He walloped the lettuce box as hard as he could. The shallow cardboard box flattened by the second blow. "Hmmm," Al said thoughtfully, wiping a drip of lettuce goo out of his eye.

He took an extra deep breath and brought the stick down with all his might on an empty toilet roll box.

THWACK!

THWACK!

THWACK!

Then he turned to the empty wine box. It was made of stronger cardboard than the other boxes. Al thwacked it a few times, but it soon crumpled as well.

THWACK!

THWACK!

THWACK!

THWACK!

THWACK!

The door between the shop and the storeroom creaked open.

Al froze. But it wasn't an angry grown-up barging though the door, it was a big, hairy dog.

"Einstein!" cried Al, closing the door quickly. "I thought you were Mum!"

Einstein sniffed suspiciously at the green dollops on the floor.

"That's it, Einstein, lick it up!" Al said, encouragingly. Einstein scooped up a slimy gloop with his long pink tongue . . . and immediately spat it out.

THPPPTH!

Einstein looked up at Al and wagged his tail. Al tickled him behind the ears.

"Yep, lettuce is yucky," Al agreed, as he tried to hide the walking stick behind his back. Einstein had a thing about sticks.

Too late! Einstein jumped up, clamped the walking stick between his jaws and trotted towards the open back door.

THUNK!

The stick caught in the doorframe. Einstein backed off. He gave the door a long, hard stare, and ran at it again.

THUNK!

Einstein dropped the stick and stared at the door in disbelief.

Al giggled. You didn't have to be a genius to work out that you needed to turn the stick to get through the door. But Einstein wasn't a genius. Well,

Einstein the dog wasn't, anyway. Al glanced round the storeroom. What could he thwack next? There were lots of things no-one had used for ages. Barbecue? Tool kit? Paint pots . . .

His twin sister Lottie burst in from the garden. She held up a large pickle jar. It had a piece of material stretched over the top, held on by a rubber band.

"Look what I found!" she said.

Lottie wanted to be a wildlife presenter on TV when she grew up. She was always in the garden studying things. Creepy crawly things. Spiders. If there was one thing Al couldn't stand, it was spiders.

Al peeped in the jar. He shuddered. A spider with a tiny body and eight very long legs was wriggling around inside.

"Spiders have been around since before the dinosaurs!" Lottie was saying. "If you look closely you can see they've got eight eyes . . ."

She held the jar up to Al's face.

PING! The elastic band snapped and the cloth covering fell off.

"**AAARGH!**" Al yelled. He jumped backwards as the spider floated to the ground on a thread. His tummy did somersaults.

"Scaredy cat!" Lottie giggled as they watched the spider crawl across the crumpled boxes. It scuttled round the green slimy globs, over the pile of iceberg lettuces and through the gap under the shop door.

"Why are you experimenting with lettuce?" Lottie asked.

"I'm not," Al told her. "I'm trying to decide what shape a time machine should be. I want to go back and meet Great Grandpa Boffin." Al was also planning to take Mum back to a time when she wasn't so tired and unhappy, but he didn't say that bit out loud. That was a secret.

"Cool!" Lottie exclaimed. "We could go back to the time of the dinosaurs! There were spiders the size of footballs in the Jurassic!"

Al tried to ignore the picture in his head. "A time machine has to take a lot of force," he went on. "I'm running an experiment about that. The lettuce just got in the way . . ."

Al took out his notebook and pencil. "I just need to make a note of the result of my experiment. Scientists have to do that. *The wine box is the strongest*," he wrote. He stuffed the notebook back into his pocket.

Lottie began to scrape green guck off the floor and into her pickle jar. "I can use this lettuce. The caterpillars will love it."

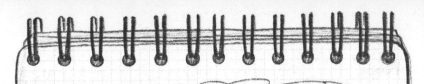

AL'S BOX EXPERIMENT

? To find out how much force a cardboard box can take before flattening. **?**

What Al used:

lettuce box

wine box

toilet roll box

+

walking stick

What Al did:

Al counted the number of walking stick hits it took to flatten each box.

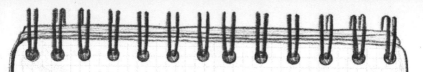

Results:

NUMBER OF HITS:

Lettuce box: 2 thwacks

Toilet roll box: 3 thwacks

Wine box: 5 thwacks

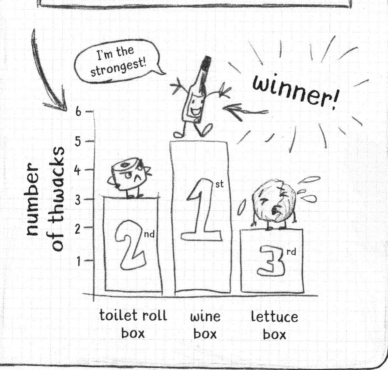

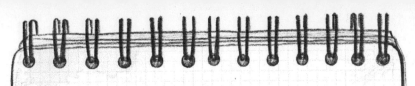

Observations:

1. Al's arm was getting tired so his last thwacks didn't have the same force as his first ones. Plus sometimes he hit the middle of the boxes and sometimes the corners.

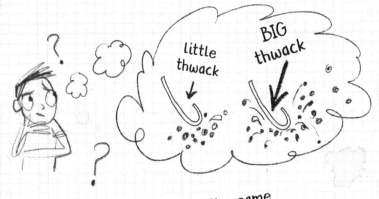

little thwack

BIG thwack

2. Try to make each thwack the same force and speed.

Measure the size and thickness of the boxes.

3. It's best if lettuce doesn't get in the way.

Yuk!

4. Or dogs who like walking sticks.

Al picked a couple of sludgy bits of lettuce off his shorts and dropped them in Lottie's jar. "I need to do more experiments," he said. "Time and space would press all over a time machine, not just whack it in one place. There are lots of shapes I haven't tried yet. Like paint tins . . ."

Lottie brushed her red hair out of her eyes. "In nature, one of the strongest things is an egg," she said thoughtfully. "They only crack when they hatch because whatever's inside pecks its way out."

"I saw Mum put a load of eggs

in the kitchen fridge . . ."
Al said. A big grin plastered
itself across his freckly
face. "We can experiment
with eggs!"

Lottie's grin mirrored Al's.

"**EGG-SPERIMENTS!**" the twins
exclaimed, jumping into the air to give
each other a high five.

Einstein raced round in circles,
barking.

"Keep that dog quiet!" shouted
a voice from next door. "He's disturbing
Precious!"

Al and Lottie looked at one another

and rolled their eyes. It was their neighbour Mrs Good. They were always getting into trouble for disturbing her pedigree cat.

"**SSSHHH!**" Lottie told Einstein. The twins knelt down and tickled him behind his ears until he calmed down and stopped barking.

"Come on, time for a few quiet egg-speriments! " said Al.

Al and Lottie Get Cracking

Lottie peered into the fridge.

"There are four boxes of eggs in here," she told Al. "Mum must be making omelette for dinner."

"She won't need that many," said Al, taking out a box.

"She won't like us wasting eggs," warned Lottie.

"We're not wasting them," said Al.

"We're using them for science!

"Now let's see how strong an egg is then." Al wrapped his fingers around one. He turned his head away, closed his eyes, and squeezed as hard as he could. Nothing happened. Al opened his eyes and examined the egg. It was in one piece!

"Wimp!" Lottie took the egg. Her face went purple with effort as she squeezed.

"Who's a wimp now?" Al grinned.

"It's really strong!" Lottie gasped.

"We're testing the shape for my time machine," Al reminded her. "We need to check the cracking point. We can do that by putting Mum's weights on top of it."

"OK." Lottie stopped squeezing and and carefully put the egg on the kitchen counter. It rolled off onto the floor.

SPLAT!

In the blink of an eye, Einstein was on it, slurping up the eggy mess and crunching up the eggshell. He wagged his tail, licked his lips and looked up hopefully for more.

"I'm not sure raw eggs are good for dogs," Lottie said, worriedly.

"Einstein's fine," Al reassured her. "Eggs that have a little red lion on them are safe to eat runny, remember?"

He took another egg. "Now, how do we stop this one from rolling?" He glanced round the kitchen.

"This'll work." Al took out a slice of bread and placed the egg sideways on it.

Lottie handed him the 50 gram weight from the stack of weights that Mum used with her old-fashioned balance scales.

The weight wibble-wobbled on the side of the egg. "It'd be easier if the egg was standing on its end," Al said.

The shop door opened and Mrs Boffin hurried in.

Al backed against the counter, hoping to hide what they were up to.

"The shop's really busy today," Mum said, helping herself to a glass of squash.

"That's good," Al said.

"It is!" Mum gave a tired smile. "I've even got help in the shop this afternoon so we can spend a bit of time together."

"Great!" Al and Lottie said together.

The bell on the shop door rang.

"Another customer! Enjoy your sandwich . . ." Mum disappeared back into the shop.

"Yummy sandwich!" joked Lottie as

Al stacked up five bread slices and stuck his elbow into the middle of them. He popped the egg into the hole so it stood up. Then he carefully balanced the weight on the end of the egg and let go. The weight slid off.

PLUNK! Five slices of bread and the raw egg plopped onto the floor.

"Mangled molecules!" Al murmured as Einstein instantly gobbled it all up.

Al looked around the kitchen again. "This'll work better," he said, pushing a third egg into the sugar jar. He added the weight. The egg disappeared.

"Too much sugar," Lottie said.

Al grabbed a spoon and scooped sugar onto the kitchen counter. He stopped scooping when the egg was sitting on the bottom of the sugar jar. There was enough sugar left around it that it didn't fall over.

"These weights fit the sugar jar just right." Lottie carefully balanced a

100 gram weight on the egg, followed by the 200 gram weight.

"Wow! This egg is really strong. It would make a great time machine!" Al said, accidentally dropping the 500 gram weight on top . . .

SPLAT!

The egg gave way.

"It would have taken more weight if I hadn't dropped that one!"

Al fished out the weights and the bits of shell, then scraped up the spilled sugar in his hands and dumped it back in the jar on top of the eggy gloop.

"If one egg's that strong, how much weight can a whole box of eggs take?" he said excitedly, wiping his sticky hands on his shorts.

"There's only one way to find out." Lottie opened a box of six eggs and put it down on the floor. Then she placed another one next to it. Einstein wagged his tail enthusiastically.

"They're not for you," Al told him. Einstein gave a sigh and lay down with his nose on his paws.

"I'll see if they take my weight."

Lottie took off her sandals and slowly and carefully stepped up onto the eggs. "They do!!!"

"Awesome!" exclaimed Al, as Lottie stepped down from the unbroken eggs. "Try putting more weight on. I know what we can use!" He pointed to the shelf full of Mum's cookery books.

"Are you sure this is a good idea?" Lottie asked as she helped Al pile up the books on top of the open egg boxes. "Mum likes her cookery books."

"'Course it is!" Al said confidently. "It'll take my weight too. Watch!"

He leapt on top of the books.

Raw egg and bits of shell splatted all over Mum's cookery books, the floor and up the back of Al's legs. Lottie wiped a droplet of egg gloop from the end of her nose.

"Yuurgh!" the twins exclaimed together.

"Mum'll be upset," Lottie said as they stared in horror at the state of the kitchen.

"Not if she doesn't know," Al said. "Einstein!" he called loudly.

"Woof!" Einstein jumped to his feet and began licking up the mess.

AWFUL WARNING:

Raw egg can contain germs called salmonella. Salmonella can make you very sick. The risk of an egg being contaminated is very, very low, but to be on the safe side, DON'T EAT RAW EGG like Einstein!

Cook eggs until the whites and yolks are firm. Salmonella bacteria is destroyed by heat. It's also destroyed by soap and water. So thoroughly WASH everything that comes into contact with raw eggs – especially your hands.

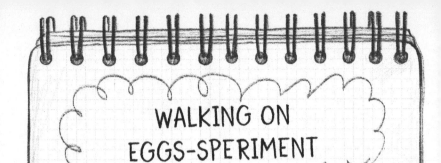

WALKING ON EGGS-SPERIMENT

To find out how much weight a box of eggs can take before cracking.

What Al used:

Two boxes of six eggs, with the lid open

x 2

Mum's cookery books (or any other books)

Al and Lottie's feet

→

Stinky!

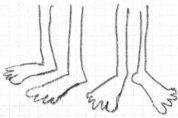

What Al and Lottie did:

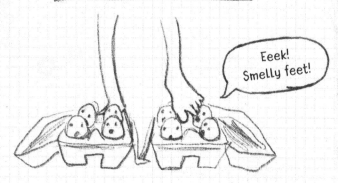

Eeek! Smelly feet!

Lottie took off her shoes and gently put one foot on each box of eggs.

Al piled up Mum's cookery books (all nineteen) on the eggs, then he jumped on top.

Results:

The eggs didn't break when Lottie stepped on them!

The eggs didn't break when Al piled up the books on them.

The eggs DID break when Al jumped on top.

Observations:

1. Eggs are strong when weight is added slowly and carefully.

2. Eggs break when there is sudden force on them.

3. Broken eggs are gloopy and stick to cookery books and bare legs.

The dome shape of the egg distributes weight and pressure from the top to the whole of the structure. Domes are strong and are often used as the roof of big buildings.

Try it at home! What will you discover?
WARNING: ASK A GROWN-UP FIRST! IT COULD GET MESSY!
Try to use eggs past their sell-by date so as to not waste food like the twins. And don't try this on the living room carpet!

Great Eggspectations

Al tried not to wriggle as Einstein's warm tongue slurped egg off his bare legs. "There must be a way to protect eggs from sudden force," he said, holding out the cookery books one by one for Einstein to lick.

Lottie picked up the mangled and dripping remains of the egg boxes. "This looks like one of Einstein's doggy chews!" she said as she dropped them in the bin.

"A stronger box would have saved the eggs when I jumped on them," Al said thoughtfully. It was as if a light bulb had gone off in his head. He knew just what to use for his next egg-speriment. He rushed off to grab some plastic bricks from the heap on his bedroom floor.

When he got back, Einstein was in his basket, lying on his back with his hairy tummy bulging. He was snoring gentle little doggy snores. It looked as if he'd licked the floor clean. Phew! Mum would never know!

Lottie was sitting cross-legged on the floor with an egg in one hand and a roll of tinfoil in the other.

"I think squishy wrapping will work better than a solid box," she said, crumpling the tinfoil around the egg. She kept on going until there was nothing left on the roll. "This egg is as big as an ostrich's," she giggled.

AWESOME EGG FACTS:

Eggs are laid by female birds, reptiles, amphibians, fish and a few mammals, including the duck-billed platypus. Ostriches lay the largest eggs of all living creatures, but the largest eggs ever were laid by the extinct Elephant Bird that lived in Madagascar. Its eggs were even bigger than those laid by dinosaurs!

Harriet the hen, from Essex, laid the world's largest hen's egg in 2010. It was over 23cm in diameter.

Lottie began to wrap another egg in clingfilm. Al took an egg out of the box and sat down beside her. "My egg will be better than yours!" he told his sister, as he clicked his brightly-coloured bricks into a box shape around it.

"Egg contest!" Lottie challenged him. "Three eggs each. There's bubble wrap and sticky tape in my room." She jumped to her feet and hurried off with an egg in her hand.

"You're on!" Al spotted the remainder of the bread loaf. He hollowed out an egg-shaped space in the middle of the bread slices, inserted an egg and carefully put the loaf back together. He re-tied the bread bag with the twisty tag, but it didn't look very strong, so he put the whole lot inside

another plastic bag, trapping lots of air inside it when he tied it up.

One more to go . . . Al threw open the kitchen cupboard doors. Rice! He opened the new bag of rice, dropped in the egg and re-sealed the packet with a sticking plaster from the first-aid box.

There were plenty of first-aid supplies so he stuck sticking plasters all over one egg and swaddled another in cotton wool and bandages. As he wrapped, a nursery rhyme popped into his head.

"Humpty Dumpty sat on a wall, Humpty Dumpty had a great fall. All the King's horses and all the King's men Couldn't put Humpty together again!" he hummed.

"Would Humpty Dumpty have broken if he'd been wrapped up like an Egyptian mummy?" Al wondered aloud.

"Maybe not if they removed his insides and stuffed him full of sawdust and herbs and stuff like they did then," Lottie said cheerfully as she appeared at his side.

"We don't have time to try that!"

Al said regretfully. "Here, I made this for you." He handed his sister one of the extra first-aid eggs.

"Thanks!"

The twins lined up their wrapped eggs on the kitchen counter.

"How shall we test them?" Al asked.

"Kick them," Lottie suggested.

"You kick harder than me," Al complained. "And even if only one of us kicks, you can't tell if each kick is the same."

"Let me think . . ." Lottie fell silent.

The nursery rhyme popped into Al's head again. "Humpty Dumpty sat on a wall," he sang, without really knowing he was doing it.

"Humpty Dumpty had a great fall!" Lottie joined in.

The twins looked at one another.

"Humpty Dumpty had a great fall!" they repeated together.

"We could push the eggs off the counter," Lottie said. "That way the height would be the same."

"It's not a great fall, though," Al murmured. "Let's take them upstairs. If we hold our hands out of a window and let them drop, the height and the force will be the same."

"Mum's told us not to lean out of windows!" said Lottie. "Are you sure this is worth the trouble we'll get into if she finds out? You're not really trying to invent a time machine to go back and meet Great Grandpa Boffin, are you?"

Al took a deep breath. "I'd like to meet him. But I'm really doing it for Mum," he whispered. "To take her back to the time before Dad died."

"That was three whole years ago. If we went with her, we'd go back to being five!" Lottie said.

"The important thing is that Mum would be happy again!" said Al.

"That's very important," Lottie agreed.

"Secret?" said Al.

"Secret," said Lottie, linking her little finger with his.

Al gathered up his eggs. "The back bedroom window on the Goods' side. If we drop the eggs out of that, they'll land on our side of the fence and no one will know!" he said confidently.

Plans Get Scrambled

The tiny back bedroom was crammed full of wonderful things the family had inherited from Great Grandpa Boffin. Al edged round a bookcase filled with dusty old science books, squeezed through a heap of carefully-labelled boxes, and eased round a big old telescope that was set up in front of the open window.

"First, I'll drop an ordinary egg to see what happens," Al said, scratching his itchy nose.

Lottie raised her eyebrows. "Never heard of gravity?" she teased.

"We need to compare it with the other eggs to see what difference the wrappings make," Al explained.

AWFUL WARNING: GRAVITY

Gravity is the force that pulls everything towards the Earth. DO NOT lean out of windows! Gravity will make you fall. SPLAT!

AWESOME SCIENCE FACT: GRAVITY

Gravity is really useful. If it didn't exist, everyone and everything on Earth would whizz off into Space unless it was tied down. That might be fun for a while, but would probably get to be a nuisance.

Being careful not to lean out too far, Al stretched his arm out of the window – just as Mrs Good opened the door to her conservatory. Al was so startled the egg flew out of his hand.

"Oh, no!" Lottie gasped.

The egg splatted on the gutter on the corner of the house and landed with a squidgy **SPLOP** on the Boffins' side of the fence.

"Phew, lucky it didn't hit next door," Al breathed.

But a few eggy drips had plopped onto the glass roof of the Goods' conservatory.

"Go away, you horrid pigeons!" Mrs Good shouted. The twins ducked down beneath the windowsill as she looked up.

They heard the gentle voice of Mr Good call, "What's the matter, my sweet?"

"It's those dirty pigeons, dear!" Mrs Good sighed loudly. "They're dropping their mess all over the conservatory. Really, Harold, you should do something about them. And the slugs. Just look at what the slugs have done to my hostas. They've stripped them bare!"

"What's a hosta?" whispered Al.

"A plant with green stripy leaves," Lottie whispered back. "Very tasty if you're a slug."

"It's so hard to keep everything clean and nice. It makes one despair!" Mrs Good sighed again. "Where's Precious? I don't want any nasty pigeon poop dirtying her pretty fur. Precious!

Precious! Come to Mumsie, my darling!" she trilled in a high-pitched sing-song voice.

"Let the cat be, Mildred," Mr Good called. "Come inside, my sweet. I'll make you a lovely cup of Earl Grey tea to calm your nerves."

There was a loud click as the conservatory door shut.

Al peeked over the windowsill.

"It's OK. She's gone inside. Just make sure nothing else hits that gutter."

He picked up the plastic brick egg in one hand and the rice egg in the other.

Lottie grabbed her tinfoil egg and bubble wrap egg.

They held out their hands.

"On target?" Al asked. Lottie nodded. Al began the countdown.

"Ten-nine-eight-seven-six-five-four-three-two-

"ONE!"

ATISHOO!

Al sneezed at the very moment they let go.

The eggs bounced off each other.

"Mangled molecules!" Al groaned. He and Lottie watched with horror as plastic bricks and rice rained down on the Goods' conservatory in an eggy shower.

Mrs Good stomped outside. "What on earth . . .?" she began.

Rice and egg dripped down her neck.

"**EEK!**" Mrs Good screamed.

The tinfoil egg and the bubble wrap egg dropped on her head.

"**EEK! EEK!**" Mrs Good shrieked. Egg was dripping from her nose and short grey hair.

Al and Lottie bumped heads in their hurry to duck out of sight.

"**OWWWW!**" they yelled.

"You!" shouted Mrs Good. "I should have known it was you two. I'm coming to see your mother **RIGHT NOW!!!**"

"Uh-oh." Al and Lottie looked at one another.

"Quick, finish the experiment before it gets shut down!" Al said, tossing the bread egg, the clingfilm egg and the first-aid eggs out of the window.

"So much for carefully dropping the eggs," Lottie groaned, as they watched the eggs land next door.

Eggsplosions!

"Al! Lottie! Get down here at once!"

Mrs Boffin's voice floated up from the kitchen.

"I hope Mrs Good's not too cross," Lottie said as they slowly made their way down the stairs.

Mrs Good was standing in the middle of the kitchen with her hands on her hips. She was splatted with egg

and shaking with rage. As she quivered, grains of rice slid out of her hair and off her green tweed jacket and skirt and pattered onto the kitchen floor.

Einstein opened an eye and trotted over to lick them up.

Mrs Good ground her teeth.

"Sit down, Mrs Good. I'll make you a nice cup of tea," Mum said, going over to the sink to fill up the kettle.

Mrs Good lowered herself onto a kitchen chair.

"Now, why don't you tell us what's the matter," Mum went on.

"It's . . . it's . . ." Mrs Good spluttered.

She seemed to be finding it hard to find the right words. "They . . . I . . . **LOOK AT THE STATE OF ME!**"

Mum gave the twins a hard stare. "What have you two been getting up to?" she asked them.

Al flashed Lottie a warning look and arranged his face into a sorry-it-was-an-accident expression. "I've been experimenting," he confessed.

"And I've been helping," Lottie added.

Mum sighed. "They're always doing this," she told Mrs Good apologetically. "They love science! They take after their Great Grandpa Boffin, you see." She gave Al and Lottie a wistful little smile. "Their dad would have been proud of them."

Mrs Good opened and closed her mouth, but only a strangled squeak came out.

Lottie hung her head. "Al's experiment got a bit messy. We're really sorry. We didn't mean to upset you, Mrs Good."

"Really, really sorry!" Al echoed.

Mrs Good made a spluttering noise that might have been her clearing her throat.

"It's not just me, you know," she said indignantly. "Precious gets upset when I get upset. Cats are very sensitive."

Einstein's ears pricked up at the mention of the word cat.

"At first I thought it was those pigeons!" Mrs Good shuddered. "But it was you! You got this mess all over me, and all over my garden!"

"Al and Lottie, I'm very disappointed in you both." Mum sighed as she filled the teapot. "You know I trust you to behave sensibly while I'm busy in the shop. I thought scientists were careful not to make too much mess!"

"Not all of them!" Al said eagerly. "Alexander Fleming would never have discovered penicillin if he'd always cleaned everything up!"

Mum raised her eyebrows.

AWESOME SCIENCE FACT: PENICILLIN

In 1928, Alexander Fleming got back from a holiday to find bluish mould killing off the bacteria in some of the dirty dishes he'd left piled up in his laboratory. He'd accidentally discovered the first antibiotic, penicillin!

Today, antibiotics are used to destroy the bacteria that causes infection and sickness. Before antibiotics, even a tiny cut could kill you if it got infected, so be very careful if you travel back in time!

Lottie gave Mum a hug. "Sorry. We didn't mean to cause any trouble," she said. "We'll clean up the mess."

"And we'll try not to make any more!" Al told her, crossing his fingers behind his back in case it should turn out to be a lie.

"That's all settled then." Mum poured Mrs Good some tea.

"Milk?" asked Lottie politely.

"Yes, please," Mrs Good said. Al breathed a sigh of relief. The worst was over. They'd apologised, Mum was okay with it and Mrs Good was clearly making an effort to be polite.

"Do you take sugar?" Mum handed Mrs Good a teaspoon and put the sugar jar on the table in front of her.

"Thank you," Mrs Good replied. "I'll help myself."

Al looked at Lottie in horror as Mrs Good spooned eggy sugar into her teacup, gave it a stir and took a sip.

For a moment, time seemed to stand still.

"Ga . . . ga . . . **GAH!**" Mrs Good gagged.

The room went very quiet. Einstein wandered over to Mrs Good and put his nose sympathetically in her lap.

He stretched out his neck and opened his jaws.

"**GUK, GUK, GUK,**" he joined in.

Mrs Good spat out her mouthful of tea at exactly the same moment as Einstein threw up all over her shiny shoes.

BLEERGH!

Al looked at Lottie. "This is when we could really do with a time machine!" he murmured, as Einstein wagged his tail and started to lick eggy puke off Mrs Good's shoes.

Eggs-it Strategy

Mrs Good jumped to her feet with a strangled eek! She ran for the door, tracking egg-puke across the kitchen floor.

Al and Lottie looked at Mum. Her shoulders were shaking. For a moment Al thought she was crying, but there was no need to worry. She was trying to stop herself from laughing! Mum

hardly ever laughed these days. The twins grinned at one another. Maybe she doesn't need the time machine to make her happy, thought Al.

Mum wordlessly pointed Einstein to the basket and the twins to the mop and antibacterial spray. Einstein curled up with a sigh and went to sleep.

"He just ate too much," Al reassured Lottie as they mopped and wiped up all the mess. "He'll be fine once he's slept it off."

Mum examined the surfaces and floor. They were sparkly clean.

"That'll do," she said. "Now go

and clean up the Goods' garden while I make dinner. We're having a special sort of omelette with potatoes and red peppers. A Spanish omelette." She opened the fridge door.

"Where are all the eggs?!" Mum cried.

"Umm, some of them are outside," Al admitted.

"Wha . . . a . . . t . . ." Mum began.

"We'll find them!" Lottie said as they headed for the door. They raced round and rang the Goods' doorbell.

Mr Good answered.

"We've come to clean up the mess in your garden," Lottie told him.

"Jolly good," Mr Good said. "I'll let you in through the back gate. Try not to make too much noise. Mildred is upstairs. She says she can feel a bit of a headache coming on."

"We'll be really quiet," Al promised.

They found Lottie's clingfilm, foil and bubble wrap eggs in Mrs Good's slug-eaten hostas. Al collected up his plastic bricks, while Lottie carefully unwrapped her eggs.

"These eggs are still whole!" she told Al.

"So is my double-wrapped bread egg!" Al said in amazement. "Egg-shaped is definitely the way to go for a time machine capsule!"

"I still won the contest!" Lottie reminded him.

"This time!" Al searched through the hostas for the two first-aid eggs. He pulled off the sticking plasters. The egg inside was smashed up, but the cotton wool and bandages one was only a little bit cracked.

They carefully carried the four good eggs and one cracked egg back home.

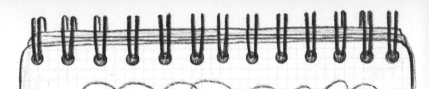

AL AND LOTTIE'S EGG DROP EGGS-PERIMENT

? To find out what materials best protect an egg from breaking when it falls. ?

What Al used:	What Lottie used:

5 eggs

Plastic bricks

Loaf of bread

Bag of rice

Sticking plasters

Extra materials:
Sticky tape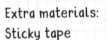

4 eggs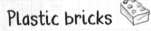

Tinfoil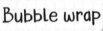

Clingfilm

Bubble wrap

Cotton wool and bandages

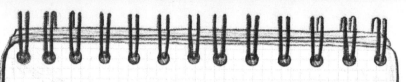

What Al did:

Here's the fun part!

Squawk!

He left one egg unwrapped. He and Lottie wrapped each of the other four eggs in a different material, then they dropped each egg out of the window.

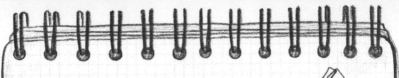

Results:

These eggs broke:
unwrapped egg,
rice, plastic brick,
sticking plasters.

This egg cracked:
cotton wool
and bandages. →

Ouch!

These eggs stayed
whole: clingfilm,
foil, bubble wrap,
bread loaf.

Observations:

1. It's best if your eggs don't
hit anything on the way
down. Check what is
below you first!

2. Eggs break when they hit (impact) the ground, unless something absorbs the impact or their fall is slowed down (like by a parachute).

Your head is egg-shaped, so wear a helmet when you ride your bike.
It will help absorb the impact if you fall off!

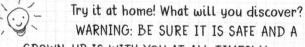

Try it at home! What will you discover?
WARNING: BE SURE IT IS SAFE AND A GROWN-UP IS WITH YOU AT ALL TIMES! You can also do this experiment from a low stool. IT COULD GET MESSY!

"We found these, Mum!" Lottie held out the eggs while Al smuggled the remains of the bread back into the loaf tin. He didn't want to waste it.

"In Mrs Good's garden?! How on earth did they get there?" Mum asked, suspiciously.

"We'll explain later," Al said. "We're still cleaning up. There are enough eggs for the omelette now, aren't there?"

Mum nodded speechlessly as the twins went back round to the Goods' house.

"I've got an idea," Lottie said, as they scooped up rice and eggshells. "Slugs don't like slithering over spiky things. We can put all this round the hostas."

"Mrs Good will be ever so pleased," agreed Al. "She might even like us after this!"

☺ ☺ ☺

Mum was waiting at the kitchen door for them to come back. She didn't look pleased.

"There'd better be a good explanation for why the pages of my

recipe book are all stuck together," she grumbled. "And why there's no tinfoil left . . . "

"Er . . . That might have something to do with my experiment . . ." Al began.

There was a sudden flapping of wings as a flock of pigeons fluttered down and landed next door.

Einstein raced out of the kitchen, barking.

"The pigeons must be after the rice!" Lottie raced after Einstein, closely followed by Al.

"Oh, no!" Al gasped. He'd forgotten to close the gate. Einstein was in the Goods' garden. There would be trouble if he saw Precious!

Mrs Good was jumping up and down, waving her arms. "Go away, you nasty pigeons!" she yelled.

WOOF WOOF WOOF! Einstein barked.

The pigeons took off.

Mr Good came out wearing his slippers and clutching a newspaper. "I thought Snoreton would be a nice peaceful village to retire to," he said. He raised his voice to be heard above the barking. **"WHAT DOES A PERSON HAVE TO DO TO GET A BIT OF PEACE AND QUIET AROUND HERE?"**

"Harold! Look at my hostas!" Mrs Good knelt down beside her plants. "They look as if they've been trampled by a herd of elephants."

Mr Good bent down and picked up a handful of rice.

"Where did this come from?" he asked. "Waste of perfectly good rice if you ask me!"

Everyone went quiet. Even Einstein.

"It isn't wasted," Lottie piped up. "The pigeons love it. It's a healthy meal for them!"

"YOU!" Mrs Good leapt to her feet and pointed a shaking finger at the twins.

Al and Lottie looked at one another.

"This is when a time machine would be good," Al murmured.

Lottie nodded. "**RUN!**" she shouted and turned for home. But . . .

Suddenly, a blur of fur shot past Al's legs, through the gate, and into the Boffins' garden. Einstein gave an excited bark and raced after it, ears flapping.

"Don't worry! Mumsie will rescue you!"
Mrs Good called, chasing after her cat.
"**STOP, EINSTEIN!**" Lottie cried.

WOOF!
WOOF!

Precious scrambled up the ivy on the wall at the back of the Boffins' garden.

She licked a paw and carefully groomed her ears as if nothing had happened.

Al, Lottie, the Goods and Einstein watched open-mouthed as she daintily tightrope-walked along the wall, back into the Goods' garden.

"Mumsie's coming, Precious!"

Mrs Good elbowed her way past the twins, followed by Mr Good.

"**YOU HAVEN'T HEARD THE LAST OF THIS!**" she said threateningly.

Al quickly closed the garden gate behind them.

The kitchen smelled of sizzling onions, peppers and egg. Mum was singing along to a cheesy love song on the radio.

Al breathed a sigh of relief. She hadn't noticed the commotion outside.

"That brings back happy memories!'" Mum sighed. "Go upstairs and wash your hands," she told the twins. "The Spanish omelette is almost ready. I'm just about to make some toast to go with it. And maybe a bit of salad . . ."

Al and Lottie raced upstairs, with Einstein bounding after them.

"I've had enough eggs today," Al said. "I think I'll just have the toast."

"Me too," said Lottie.

There was a strangled squawk from the kitchen.

"WHAT SORT OF EXPERIMENT WERE YOU DOING?" Mum yelled. **"THE BREAD'S IN BITS. AND WHERE'S THE LETTUCE???!!!"**

The doorbell rang. Al and Lottie paused at the top of the stairs to see who it was.

"Can I help you, Mrs Good?" Mum asked.

"Mangled molecules! How do we get out of this?" Al whispered to Lottie.

"AL! LOTTIE! GET DOWN HERE THIS MINUTE!" Mum yelled.

The twins fled into the bathroom.

Einstein tried to hide behind Al's legs.

"Wish I had invented that time machine!" Al sighed.

"Wish you had, too!' Lottie agreed. "You're not going to give up, are you?"

"Give up?" Al straightened up and looked at himself in the mirror. His hair was all over the place and there was a gleam in his eyes.

"I, Al Boffin, am a scientist!" he said. Maybe he should get himself some glasses to complete the look.

"Scientists **NEVER** give up!" said Al. He patted the notebook in his pocket as he, Lottie and Einstein reluctantly slunk downstairs to face Mum and Mrs Good.

"I **HAVE** to keep experimenting!"

EGGSTRA EGG DROP
EGG-SPERIMENTS

(?) Experiment to find out if changing HOW the egg drops makes a difference. (?)

1. Try using a parachute to slow down the egg drop.

Put the egg in a box, surrounded by some soft materials such as bubble wrap, cotton wool or crumpled newspapers. Tape the handles of an old plastic shopping bag to the side of the box.

When you drop it, keep the shopping bag facing upwards so it can fill up with air on the way down. This slows down the egg's fall.

? What happens? How does it compare with the previous experiment? ?

Drop the egg lightly. Don't toss it down with extra force.

WARNING: LEANING OUT OF WINDOWS IS VERY DANGEROUS!

 TIP: If you tightly seal the egg in a small plastic bag first, you can give your egg to a grown-up to cook even if it cracks so that you are not wasting food.

2. Try softening the landing site.

 More eggs will survive if the drop zone is grass rather than stone or another hard surface.

Try dropping your egg into a big box full of bubble wrap packaging.

Or try catching it in a fishing net, or a big towel held out by your friends!

What happens?

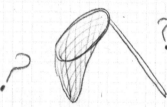

Slowing down the egg drop and softening the landing site both help to reduce the force of the impact on the fragile eggshell and stop it from cracking!

 WARNING: BE SURE IT IS SAFE AND A GROWN-UP IS WITH YOU! EGG-SPERIMENTING COULD GET MESSY!

Look out for Al's next adventure,
coming in June 2018!

SPLASH DOWN!

AWESOME SCIENCE RECIPE:

Take one family

and one
BIG IDEA

Plus some straws, Mum's
bucket, the next door
neighbour's knickers,
one cat + one hot dog

NOW ADD WATER!